ACTIVITY BOOK

Santillana
INTENSIVE
English

6

✸Santillana USA

ISBN 1-58105-368-1 Activity Book 6

Santillana USA Publishing Company, Inc.
2105 N.W. 86th Avenue
Miami, FL 33122

How to Use This Book

The goal of *Santillana Intensive English* (*SIE*) is to assist learners in acquiring communication skills as well as the academic language that is necessary to achieve in the all-English classroom.

Each grade-level of *SIE* is divided into 12 theme units. Each unit contains ten lessons found on individual Lesson Cards – 120 cards in each grade. To teach each lesson, the teacher need only follow the lesson plans on the Lesson Card. Each card uses a clear three-step approach: Teach, Practice and Apply, and Extend.

The goal of the *SIE* Activity Books is to reinforce the concepts, vocabulary, and language structures taught. The Home School Connection, an important part of every lesson, enables students to share their learning with family members. When finished, the Activity Book pages will serve as a permanent record of student achievement and may be incorporated into assessment portfolios.

The Activity Book tasks should be assigned after each lesson is completed. Students should complete them independently. The lessons may be completed in class or assigned for home-work. They should be corrected and returned to students. This procedure may be modified to handle the case of students at different stages of language acquisition in the same classroom. Following are brief descriptions of the stages of language acquisition (see Stephen D. Krashen, *The Natural Approach: Language Acquisition in the Classroom*, Upper Saddle River, NJ: Prentice Hall, 1996).

Stage 1, Preproduction
Learners have minimal or no comprehension of English. They may participate in activities by saying yes or no or by using gestures.

Stage 2, Early Production
Learners have some comprehension of English. They participate in activities by responding with single words or short phrases in English.

Stage 3, Speech Emergence
Learners participate in activities by responding with longer phrases and complete sentences. They can engage in conversation, narrate events, and express opinions.

Stage 4, Intermediate Fluency
Learners can deal with a wider variety of topics in conversation, can speak extemporaneously, and can manipulate shades of meaning.

The following chart compares the Activity Book tasks with learners at the four stages of language acquisition. The filled-in boxes indicate that those learners can do those tasks.

	fill-in	label (labels given)	match	write sentence	draw	label (labels not given)	write paragraph
Preproduction	shaded	shaded	shaded		shaded	shaded	
Early Production	shaded	shaded	shaded	shaded	shaded	shaded	
Speech Emergence	shaded	shaded	shaded	shaded	shaded	shaded	shaded
Intermediate Fluency	shaded	shaded	shaded	shaded	shaded	shaded	shaded

The tasks that are most challenging for Preproduction and Early Production learners are writing sentences and paragraphs. Students at those stages can still participate in these writing activities if some oral preparation is done in class and they work in pairs with students at a higher stage of language acquisition. Oral preparation might include a discussion of the subject, writing the key words on the board for students to copy and learn, and providing oral and written examples. The lower-level learner might begin by copying the correct work of a more proficient partner but should be encouraged to produce original writing as well. As the academic year progresses, less pair work should be necessary. If more proficient students are not available to work with the lower-level students, adult or student tutors or the classroom teacher may be asked to work with them.

The Home School Connection activity may also be utilized by adult or student tutors to help move learners at the Speech Emergence and Intermediate Fluency stages to higher levels of proficiency. The tutor should be asked to participate as if he or she were the family member. The learner can practice the task several times if necessary before attempting it with a family member.

In all these ways, the *SIE* Activity Books contribute to the overall program goal of mastery of social and academic English in record time.

My name is _____ .   I am a _____ .

She is a _____ .   He is a _____ .   She is the _____ .

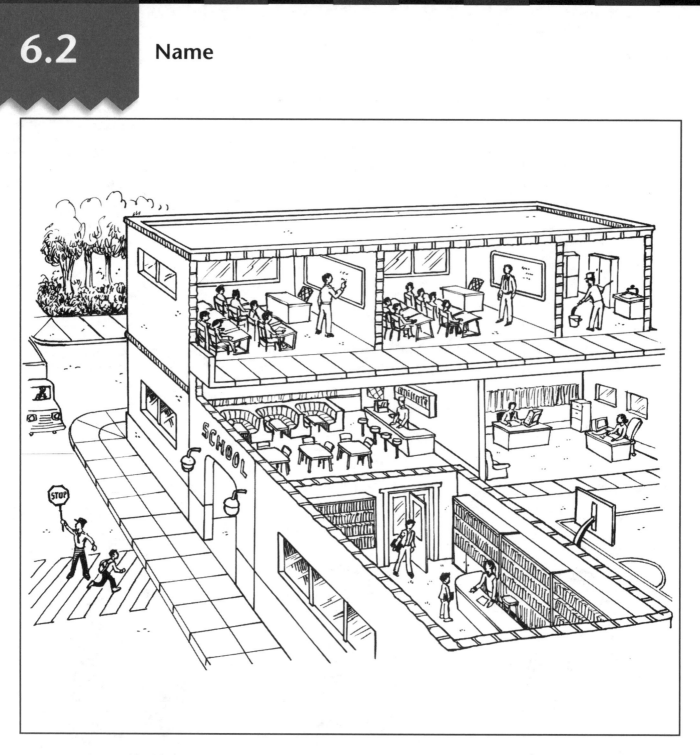

Use these words to label the people and places at school.

cafeteria	librarian	playground	secretary
crossing guard	janitor	principal	teacher

Have students share the labeled map of a school with family members. Students should ask family members to tell them about what their own school was like when they were the student's age.

Name

Write the correct phrase from the box under each picture.

get in line	hello	raise your hand
sit down	stand up	work with

Home School Connection

Students should demonstrate each action and repeat appropriate phrases for family members. Encourage them to ask family members to participate in giving and responding to commands.

Name

Write the correct word from the box under each picture.

cafeteria	library
classroom	office

Complete the sentence by writing the correct word in the blank.

1. The principal is in the _____ .

2. We eat in the _____ .

3. Books are in the _____ .

4. Our teacher is in the _____ .

Name

Write the correct word from the box under each picture.

| basketball | softball | track |
| soccer ball | basketball hoop | volleyball |

_____

_____

_____

_____

_____

_____

Write the correct word on the line.

1. We play _____ with a bat and a ball.
2. We shoot hoops with a _____ .
3. We kick the ball on a _____ field.
4. We run on the _____ .
5. We throw the basketball in the _____ .
6. We hit the _____ over the net.

Home School Connection

Have students name the sports equipment for a family member. Then, have them ask the family member to name a piece of sports or play equipment while they pantomime its use.

Connect each word to its matching picture.

drinking fountain

straw

milk

napkin

fork

knife

spoon

table

bench

trashcan

Write a word in each blank space so that the sentence tells about the picture.

1. Our arrival time at school is _____ .

2. We go _____ to our classroom to study, speak and write.

1. We are on the playground for _____ .

2. This comes after _____ _____ .

3. We go _____ for this.

1. We eat in the _____.

2. This comes after _____ _____.

3. We go _____ for this.

Home School Connection

Ask students to list orally the school events of class time, recess, and lunch in the cafeteria for a family member. Encourage the students to put events in order as well as use the terms "outside" and "inside" in their oral list.

Name

Connect each word to its matching picture. Then, beneath each picture, write a sentence about that picture.

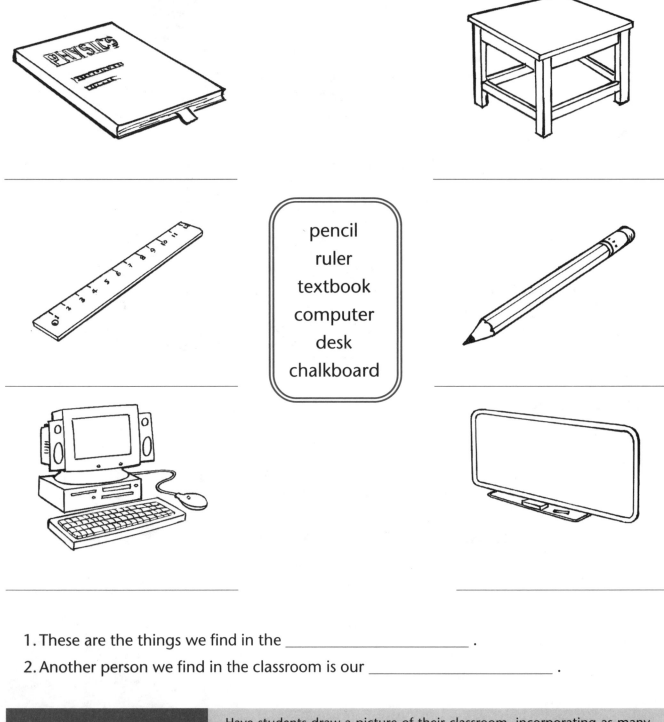

pencil
ruler
textbook
computer
desk
chalkboard

_____

1. These are the things we find in the _____ .

2. Another person we find in the classroom is our _____ .

Home School Connection

Have students draw a picture of their classroom, incorporating as many of the objects from the above list as possible. Encourage them to share their drawing with a family member, naming each object in the drawing.

Connect each word to its matching picture.

$+$

$\times$

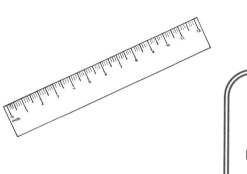

$=$

addition
division
multiplication
ruler
subtraction
fraction
equal
number
problem

$-$

37

$4 + 1 =$

$\dfrac{1}{4}$

$\div$

1. These are the things I find in _____.

2. When I complete a problem, I should _____ _____ _____.

Home School Connection

Ask students to share some of their work in mathematics and describe the operations and computation on their page, using as many of the above vocabulary words as possible.

Write the correct word or phrase from the box under each picture.

letter	question mark	comma
paragraph	period	sentence

G

_____

,

_____

We went home.

_____

Carl and I went to see the soccer game. We were at the soccer field before the game started. I was glad we were there in time to get a good seat.

_____

?

_____

.

_____

Home School Connection

Have students take home a textbook or a paper they have written and identify the symbols and terms for a family member. Students should ask the family member to quiz them on the symbols and terms.

Name

Complete the sentence under each picture with the correct word from the box.

> animals   buildings   weather
> plants   water   people

_____ is a part of our environment.

_____ are a part of our environment.

_____ are a part of our environment.

_____ is a part of our environment.

_____ are a part of our environment.

_____ are a part of our environment.

Home School Connection

Have students share the words and descriptions on this page with a family member. They should ask a family member to help them name other things that are a part of their environment.

Each of the words in the box is about something in people's home environment. Connect each word in the box to its matching picture. Then, beneath each picture, write a sentence about that picture.

kitchen
apartment
mobile home
bedroom
bathroom
house

Home School Connection

Encourage students to share the information they have about our home environments with a family member, naming the objects on this page as well as any other home environment objects or features they may recall.

Name

Use the words from the box to label the picture.

street	video store	signal	corner
bakery	stop sign	barbershop	grocery store

Name

In the space below, draw a picture of your family. Use the words in the box below to label each family member.

mother	sister	aunt	father
brother	nephew		grandmother
uncle	niece	grandfather	cousin

Home School Connection

Encourage students to share their drawings with a family member, labeling the people in their family as they share.

Write a sentence about your family or a family you know using each word or phrase above the sentence line.

family

1. _____

_____

ancestor

2. _____

_____

born

3. _____

_____

custom

4. _____

_____

foreign

5. _____

_____

immigrate

6. _____

_____

relatives

7. _____

_____

Use the words from the box to label the picture.

gas station	library	restaurant	fire department
post office		movie theater	hospital
school	supermarket	park	police station

Home School Connection

Encourage students to take a further walk with a family member, naming the things they see on the walk.

Write the correct word from the box under each picture.

beach	lake	mountain
river	park	mall

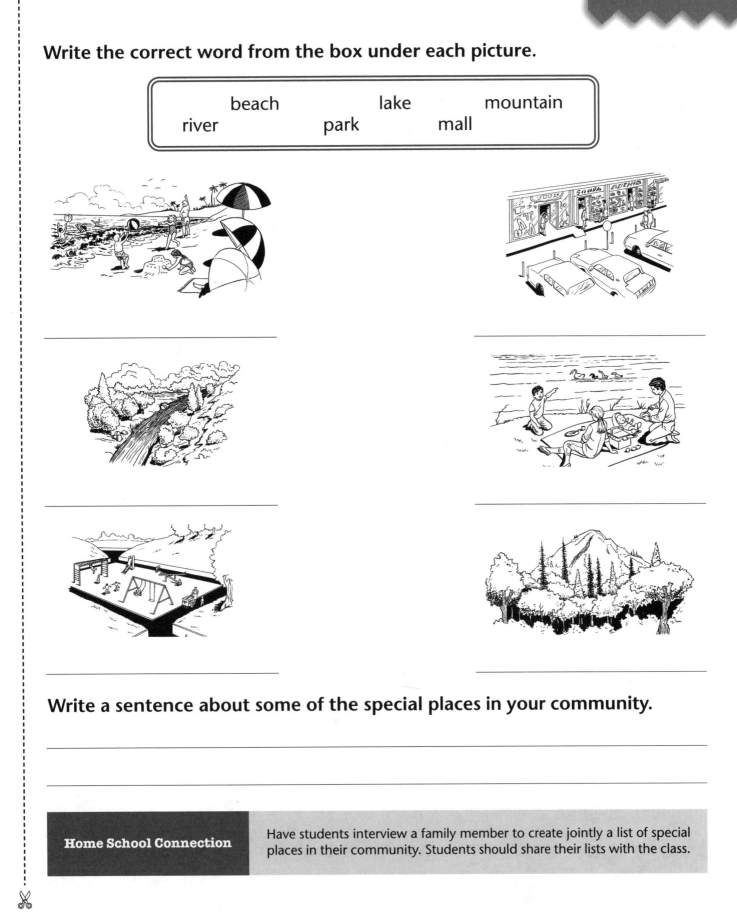

_____   _____

_____   _____

_____   _____

Write a sentence about some of the special places in your community.

_____

_____

Home School Connection

Have students interview a family member to create jointly a list of special places in their community. Students should share their lists with the class.

Write the correct word from the box under each picture.

| police officer | letter carrier | nurse |
| dentist | fire fighter | doctor |

_____   _____

_____   _____

_____   _____

Write the correct word on the line.

1. A _____ _____ brings me the mail.

2. A _____ helps me keep my teeth clean.

3. A _____ helps me if I am sick.

Name

Write each word from the box in the correct category. You may use each word more than once.

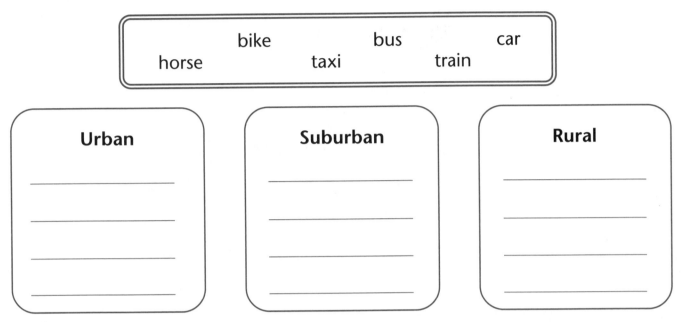

bike   bus   car
horse   taxi   train

Urban	Suburban	Rural
____	____	____
____	____	____
____	____	____
____	____	____

Would you rather live in an area that is urban, suburban, or rural? Write a paragraph about where you would like to live and why you would like to live there.

_____

_____

_____

_____

_____

_____

_____

Home School Connection   Have students ask a family member about other places they may have lived. Have the student ask where they would like to live and why.

Name

Color the state where you live red. Write the name of your state on the map. Label the compass rose on the map with North, South, East, and West.

United States of America

Complete the sentences below.

1. I live in the state of _____ .

2. The city or town where I live is _____ .

3. Our state bird is the _____ .

4. Our state flower is the _____ .

5. Our state tree is the _____ .

Imagine that you are on Planet M where spoken and written language does not exist. The only way to communicate with the people on this planet is by drawing pictures. Choose one of the three statements from the box and draw a picture or pictures to communicate with the beings on Planet M.

> I need something to eat.   Where is your home?
> Please help me find my space ship.

Home School Connection

Encourage students to ask a family member to guess what the student is trying to say in his or her drawing.

Name

You have learned that languages change. Look at the four pictures below. If the picture shows something that can cause language to change, use the word below the picture in a sentence at the bottom of the page.

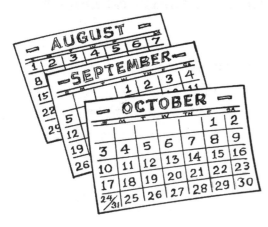

Time

Money

Buildings

Geography

1. _____ can cause languages to change.
2. _____ can cause languages to change.

Home School Connection

Encourage students to demonstrate to a family member what they know about how languages change.

You have learned that there are groups or families of languages. Each of the languages listed below belongs in one of the four language families in the boxes. Write the name of each language with the correct language family. The first one is done for you.

German	Korean	Italian	Navajo
English	Aztec	Sioux	Swahili
Spanish	Chinese	Hawaiian	Hebrew
Arabic	Masai	Eskimo	Japanese

African Language Family

Masai

_____

_____

_____

American Language Family

_____

_____

_____

Asian and Pacific Language Family

_____

_____

_____

Indo-European Language Family

_____

_____

_____

Home School Connection

Have students share the information they have on language families and ask a family member if he or she knows of another language and whether it might fit into one of the above families.

Name

Find out about the different languages that are around you. Write the names of ten students in your class in the table below. Next to each student's name, write the language or languages they already know, and English, which they are learning. The first one has been done for you.

	Name	Language	Learning
1.	Jessica	Vietnamese	English
2.			
3.			
4.			
5.			
6.			
7.			
8.			
9.			
10.			

Which language is spoken by the most people on your list? _____

Home School Connection

Encourage students to ask a family member about languages other than their own that they may encounter at work or away from the home. Have students create a list of these languages and share them with the class.

You have learned about Braille, a reading and writing system for blind persons. Braille is made up of raised dots that represent letters. Below is the Braille alphabet. Use it to write your name in Braille.

a b c d e f g h i j k l
m n o p q r s t u v w x
y z

_____
Your Name - First Try

_____
Your Name - Second Try

Name

Connect each word to the correct picture.

artist
music
statue
painting

Have students look through a magazine, book, or newspaper with a family member, identifying other examples of the arts.

In the two boxes, make a list of the foods you like and the foods you don't like. Then, complete the sentences at the bottom of the page.

Foods I Like	*Foods I Don't Like*
_____	_____
_____	_____
_____	_____
_____	_____
_____	_____
_____	_____
_____	_____
_____	_____
_____	_____
_____	_____
_____	_____

1. I like _____ because _____ .

2. I don't like _____ because _____ .

Home School Connection

Encourage students to help another family member prepare a meal and name each of the dishes or ingredients in English.

Each of the words in the box is about clothing. Connect each word in the box to its matching picture. Then, beneath each picture, write the correct name from the box.

suit
skirt
shoes
uniform
pants
shirt

Name

Fill in the blanks in each box.

These are the songs I like to listen to:

_____

_____

_____

_____

These are the songs
I like to dance to:

_____

_____

_____

_____

_____

_____

_____

These are the songs I like
to sing with my family:

_____

_____

_____

_____

_____

_____

These are the dances I like to do:

_____

_____

_____

_____

Home School Connection   Encourage students to share their music and dance preferences with a family member and to solicit their favorites.

Name

In the space below, draw a picture that illustrates a folk tale or story that you know. Then, share your story with a partner, using the picture to tell the story.

Name _____

Use the map of the United States of America below to answer the questions.

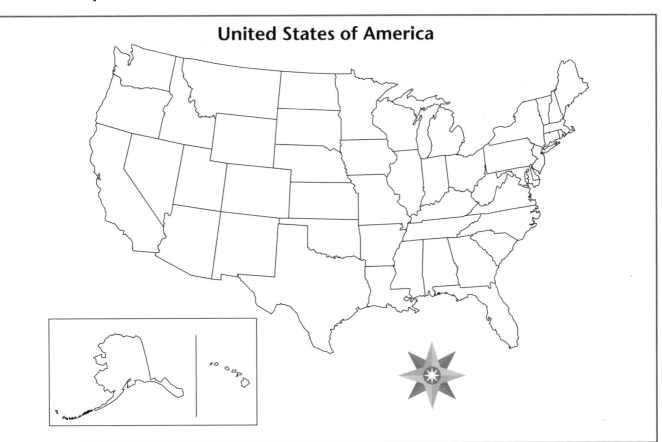

United States of America

1. Florida has two state neighbors. They are _____ and _____ .

2. California is _____ of Oregon.

3. _____ is a state that is also an island.

4. Oklahoma is _____ of Texas.

5. New York is in the _____ part of the United States.

6. Two states that are rectangles are _____ and _____ .

7. New Mexico and Arizona are south of _____ and _____ .

8. The ocean west of the United States is the _____ Ocean.

9. The ocean east of the United States is the _____ Ocean.

10. Illinois is _____ of Indiana.

Home School Connection   Have students share their map with a family member and discuss places they have visited or would like to visit in the United States.

On the map below, write the name of each continent where it should appear.

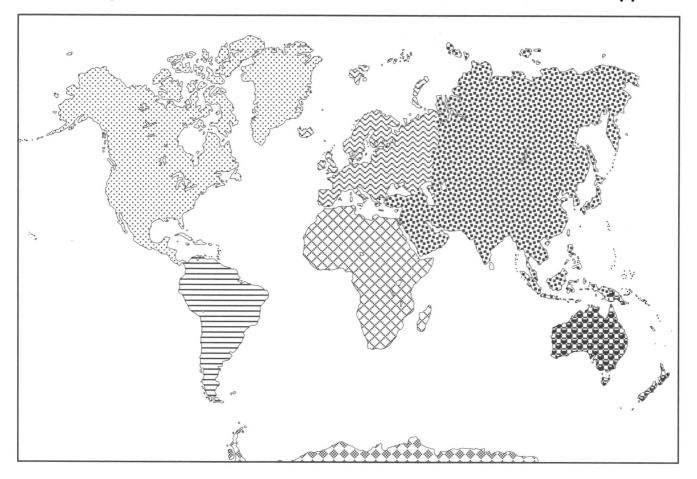

Home School Connection

Have students point out the locations of the seven continents on their map to a family member.

Write the name of each country from the box below where it should appear on this map of the western hemisphere.

Canada	Mexico	Venezuela	Panama
Chile	Cuba	Peru	Puerto Rico
Brazil	Colombia	Argentina	Costa Rica

Write the name of each continent and ocean from the box below where it should appear on this map of the world.

| Australia | Pacific Ocean | Europe |
| Africa | Indian Ocean | Asia |

Home School Connection

Have students point out the locations of the continents and oceans on their map to a family member.

Each of the words in the box has to do with life in Earth's oceans. Connect each word in the box to its matching picture. Then, beneath each picture, write a sentence about that picture.

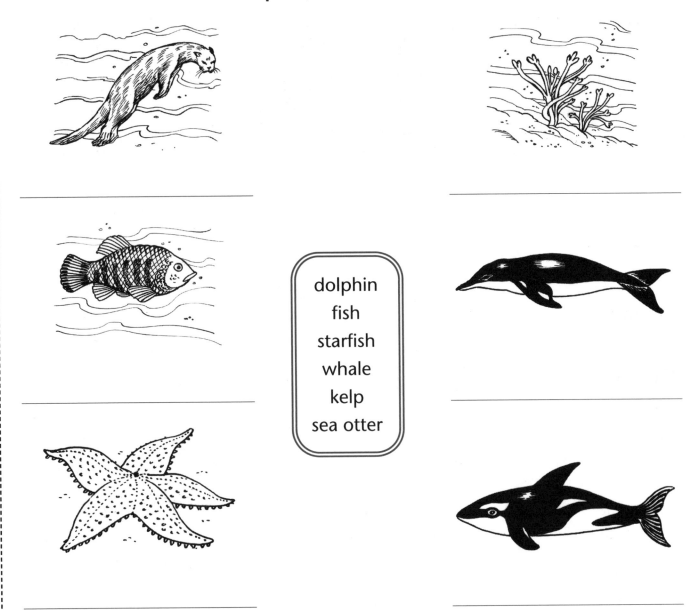

dolphin

fish

starfish

whale

kelp

sea otter

Home School Connection

Encourage students to share the information they have about ocean life with a family member, naming the sea life on this page as well as any other sea life they may recall.

Name

Write a sentence for each word.

river

1. _____

current

2. _____

tributary

3. _____

mouth

4. _____

bank

5. _____

riverboat

6. _____

wildlife

7. _____

stream

8. _____

Home School Connection

Have students create a drawing of a riverside scene. Encourage them to ask a family member to help them label the objects in the scene.

In the space below, create a drawing of the tundra. Include in your drawing all of the words listed in the box.

hawk	moss	arctic hare
polar bear	walrus	reindeer

Home School Connection   Have students describe their drawing to a family member.

Name

Using each word below, write a sentence that tells about a desert.

sand

1. _____

oasis

2. _____

temperature

3. _____

cloud

4. _____

water

5. _____

climate

6. _____

wind

7. _____

Home School Connection   Have students share their sentences with a family member and describe a desert scene.

In the space below, create a drawing of a rain forest. Include in your drawing all of the words listed in the box.

eagle	monkey	parrot
vegetation	toucan	tree

Have students describe their drawing to a family member, using the vocabulary words in their description

Name _____

Write each word in the correct box below.

swamp	flood	corn	grasses	peatland
prairie	mud flat	marsh	tidal
bog	wheat	grain	grazer	plains

Grasslands

_____

_____

_____

_____

Wetlands

_____

_____

_____

_____

Write two short paragraphs. The first should describe a grassland habitat, and the second should describe a wetland habitat.

Grassland Habitat

_____
_____
_____
_____

Wetland Habitat

_____
_____
_____
_____

Home School Connection   Have students share what they have learned about wetlands and grasslands with a family member.

Label the layers of the earth. Color the mantle yellow, color the lithosphere green, and color the core red.

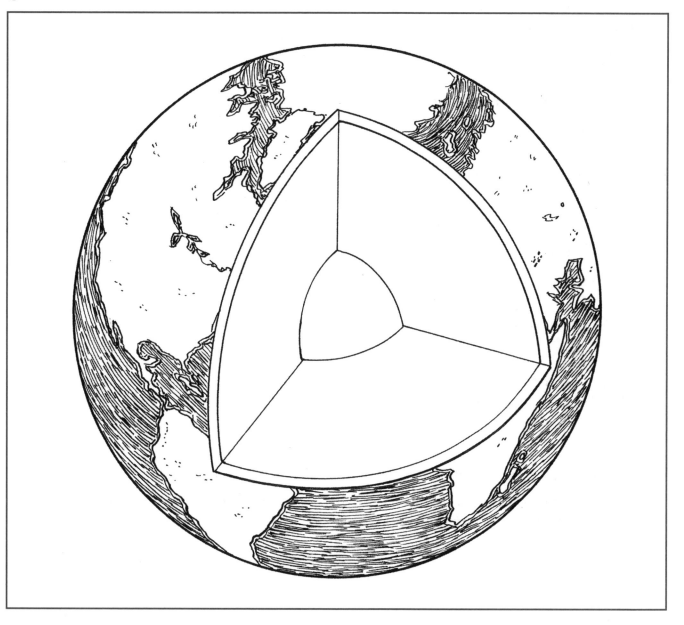

1. The solid, outer layer of the Earth is called the _____.

2. The middle section of the Earth is a hot, partly liquid layer called the _____.

3. The dense metallic center of the Earth is called the _____.

Home School Connection   Encourage students to share the information they have learned about the Earth's layers with a family member.

Name _____

Use what you have learned to complete the sentences. Check (✓) the box next to the correct answer.

1. The solid, outer layer of Earth is called the _____.

    ☐ lithosphere   ☐ core

2. The lithosphere is broken into about 20 large pieces called _____.

    ☐ the mantle   ☐ tectonic plates

3. The partly liquid layer that is below the lithosphere is called the _____.

    ☐ core   ☐ mantle

4. Tectonic plates float on the mantle much like _____.

    ☐ a fish swimming through water   ☐ rafts floating on water

5. As they float, tectonic plates move toward or away from each other very _____.

    ☐ quickly   ☐ slowly

6. Most tectonic plates move only a _____.

    ☐ a few centimeters each year   ☐ a few kilometers each year

7. Tectonic plates are important because _____.

    ☐ their movements cause many of   ☐ they are interesting to watch as they move
      the changes on the Earth's surface

Home School Connection   Encourage students to share what they have learned about plate tectonics as well as their answers on this page with a family member.

Use what you have learned to complete the sentences. Check (✓) the box next to the correct answer.

1. The theory of continental drift was formulated by _____.

   ☐ Alfred Wegener   ☐ Alfred Nobel

2. Continental drift theory states that _____.

   ☐ Earth's continents were joined together as two large landmasses   ☐ Earth's continents were joined together as one large landmass

3. Alfred Wegener called the landmass _____.

   ☐ Europa   ☐ Pangaea

4. Wegener believed that over millions of years, Pangaea _____.

   ☐ was an important tectonic plate   ☐ broke into pieces that moved apart, forming the continents

5. One thing that Wegener used as evidence for continental drift was _____.

   ☐ the fact that the shapes of continents seemed to fit together like pieces of a puzzle   ☐ that people kept historical records that told how much continents had drifted

6. Fossils are _____.

   ☐ animals that are kept in zoos and aquariums   ☐ the remains and traces of living things from the past

7. A theory is _____.

   ☐ a number of facts that can be observed and proved   ☐ an idea that has not yet been proved

Home School Connection   Encourage students to share what they have learned about continental drift as well as their answers on this page with a family member.

Name

Imagine that you are working with Alfred Wegener in 1912 trying to convince other scientists of the theory of continental drift. Write a short paragraph telling how you would help Wegener.

_____

_____

_____

_____

_____

What if the land on Earth was all in one piece as Wegener believed it was at one time millions of years ago? Write a paragraph telling what life on Earth might be like if we lived on Pangaea.

_____

_____

_____

_____

_____

_____

Home School Connection

Have students share their paragraphs and describe what they think life might have been like on Pangaea with a family member.

Name

Use what you have learned to complete the sentences. Check (✓) the box next to the correct answer.

1. An earthquake is _____ .
   - [ ] a sudden eruption of the Earth's core
   - [ ] a sudden strong movement of the Earth's lithosphere

2. Earthquakes happen _____ .
   - [ ] along faults, or breaks in the lithosphere
   - [ ] in the center of tectonic plates

3. Many faults are located _____ .
   - [ ] where two tectonic plates meet
   - [ ] where four tectonic plates meet

4. Powerful earthquakes happened along the San Andreas fault in 1906 and 1989 when _____ .
   - [ ] an explosion took place rubbed together
   - [ ] two tectonic plates moved and

5. The San Andreas fault is found in _____ .
   - [ ] California
   - [ ] Hawaii

6. When earthquakes happen, _____ .
   - [ ] people are not aware they have taken place
   - [ ] the ground can shake, sometimes damaging buildings, bridges, and roads

7. The place on the Earth's surface that is just above the focus of an earthquake is called the _____ .
   - [ ] damage
   - [ ] epicenter

Home School Connection   Encourage students to share what they have learned about earthquakes as well as their answers on this page with a family member.

Write a sentence for each word.

lava

1. _____

magma

2. _____

explosive

3. _____

gases

4. _____

rock

5. _____

heat

6. _____

destructive

7. _____

volcano

8. _____

Home School Connection   Encourage students to share their sentences as well as what they have learned about volcanoes with a family member.

You have learned that there are three kinds of mountains: dome mountains, fault-block mountains, and folded mountains. Use what you have learned to write a paragraph that describes how each kind of mountain is formed.

dome mountain

_____

_____

_____

_____

fault-block mountain

_____

_____

_____

_____

_____

folded mountain

_____

_____

_____

_____

_____

Home School Connection | Encourage students to share their paragraphs and information about how a mountain is formed with a family member.

Name

Use what you have learned to complete the sentences. Check (✓) the box next to the correct answer.

1. Weathering is _____ .
   - [ ] the breaking down of rocks and materials on Earth's surface
   - [ ] rain falling into the ocean

2. The small bits of rock and other materials produced by weathering are called _____ .
   - [ ] stones
   - [ ] sediment

3. The process that moves sediment from one place to another is called _____ .
   - [ ] continental drift
   - [ ] erosion

4. The dropping and collecting of sediment in new places is called _____ .
   - [ ] erosion
   - [ ] deposition

5. Soil particles are classified as _____ .
   - [ ] rocks
   - [ ] sand, silt, and clay

6. Sediment can remain in one place or be carried to new places by _____ .
   - [ ] moving water, wind, glaciers, or gravity
   - [ ] tectonic plates

Write sentences about an example you have seen in the world around you of weathering or erosion.

_____

_____

_____

_____

_____

Connect each word in the box to its matching picture. Then, beneath each picture, write a sentence about that picture.

_____

_____

sand
river
beach
waves
snow
rock

_____

_____

_____

Home School Connection

Encourage students to share the information they have about erosion with a family member.

Use what you have learned to complete the sentences. Check (✓) the box next to the correct answer.

1. If erosion occurs over and over in the same place, a _____ forms where soil has been carried away.

   ☐ mountain   ☐ gully

2. In time, a gully can widen to form a _____ .

   ☐ channel   ☐ ocean

3. Many streams can join together to feed a larger stream called a _____ .

   ☐ gully   ☐ river

4. The place where a river starts is called its _____ .

   ☐ source   ☐ channel

5. River systems usually begin in _____ .

   ☐ mountains or on hills   ☐ oceans and mud flats

6. The place where a river ends is called its _____ .

   ☐ source   ☐ mouth

7. A river ends when it empties into another river or into the _____ .

   ☐ mountains   ☐ ocean

Write a paragraph about one important use of rivers.

_____

_____

_____

_____

_____

_____

Using the word or phrase above each line, write a sentence about heat energy.

waves

1. _____

conduction

2. _____

cooler

3. _____

energy

4. _____

gas

5. _____

heat

6. _____

liquid

7. _____

solid

8. _____

friction

9. _____

temperature

10. _____

Home School Connection

Have students read their sentences and share the information they have on heat energy with a family member.

Use what you have learned to complete the sentences. Check (✓) the box next to the correct answer.

1. Something that occupies space and exists as a solid, liquid, or gas is called _____ .
   - [ ] radiation
   - [ ] matter

2. The movement of heat through space is called _____ .
   - [ ] radiation
   - [ ] matter

3. In solids, heat is always transferred by _____ .
   - [ ] conduction
   - [ ] convection

4. In liquids and gases, heat is usually transferred by _____ .
   - [ ] conduction
   - [ ] convection

5. Heat is a form of _____ that results from the movement of particles.
   - [ ] convection
   - [ ] energy

6. _____ is how solid an object is.
   - [ ] Particles
   - [ ] Density

7. The repeated up-and-down movement of liquids or gases from the heating of particles is called a _____ .
   - [ ] fireplace
   - [ ] convection current

Write a paragraph about one important use of heat energy.

_____

_____

_____

_____

_____

_____

Home School Connection

Encourage students to share what they have learned about conduction, convection, and radiation as well as their answers on this page with a family member.

Using the word or phrase above each line, write a sentence about heating the earth.

solar energy

1. _____

geothermal energy

2. _____

conduction

3. _____

convection

4. _____

volcano

5. _____

geyser

6. _____

hot spring

7. _____

convection current

8. _____

sun

9. _____

visible light

10._____

Use what you have learned to complete the sentences. Check (✓) the box next to the correct answer.

1. The Earth's main source of energy is _____ .
   ☐ photosynthesis   ☐ the sun

2. Solar energy provides the Earth with _____ .
   ☐ food and water   ☐ heat and light

3. A collection of water droplets in the atmosphere is called a _____ .
   ☐ storm   ☐ cloud

4. The food-making process of plants is called _____ .
   ☐ photosynthesis   ☐ weathering

5. The sun heats water on the Earth's surface and helps turn the water into _____ .
   ☐ droplets   ☐ water vapor

6. _____ from the sun supplies the energy for photosynthesis.
   ☐ light   ☐ heat

7. Energy from the sun is called _____ .
   ☐ convection   ☐ solar energy

Write a paragraph that tells about one important use of solar energy.

_____

_____

_____

_____

_____

_____

_____

Home School Connection

Encourage students to share what they have learned about energy from the sun as well as their answers on this page with a family member.

Use what you have learned to complete the sentences. Check (✓) the box next to the correct answer.

1. A _____ is a substance that gives off energy when it is burned.

   ☐ fireplace   ☐ fuel

2. If you burn wood in a fireplace, you are releasing _____ .

   ☐ stored energy   ☐ photosynthesis

3. Coal, oil, and gas are called _____ .

   ☐ solar energy   ☐ fossil fuels

4. The food-making process of plants is called _____ .

   ☐ photosynthesis   ☐ fossil fuels

5. In the photosynthesis process, light energy from the sun is changed to _____ in plants.

   ☐ solar energy   ☐ chemical energy

Write a paragraph about the importance of fuels.

_____

_____

_____

_____

_____

_____

_____

Home School Connection   Encourage students to share what they have learned about energy from the sun as well as their answers on this page with a family member.

Name

Use what you have learned to complete the sentences. Check (✓) the box next to the correct answer.

1. An _____ is all the living and nonliving things in an environment and the interactions among them.

   ☐ energy   ☐ ecosystem

2. Plants are called _____ because they make, or produce, food for the whole ecosystem.

   ☐ producers   ☐ animals

3. The _____ is the main source of energy for most ecosystems.

   ☐ animals   ☐ sun

4. Organisms that get their food and energy by eating other organisms are called _____ .

   ☐ consumers   ☐ animals

Write each word from the box below in the correct list.

> grass   dog   duck   tree   moss
> flower   spider   bush   snake   bird

Producers	**Consumers**
_____	_____
_____	_____
_____	_____
_____	_____
_____	_____

Home School Connection   Encourage students to share what they have learned about ecosystems with a family member.

Each of the words in the box is found in an ecosystem. Connect each word in the box to its matching picture. Then, beneath each picture, write *biotic* or *abiotic* to tell what part of an ecosystem the picture represents.

animal
rock
plant
water
soil

Home School Connection   Encourage students to explain their understanding of an ecosystem to a family member.

Name

Use what you have learned to complete the sentences. Check (✓) the box next to the correct answer.

1. Products of the environment that are used by living things are called _____ .

   ☐ products   ☐ natural resources

2. Natural resources that can be replaced by nature are called _____ .

   ☐ renewable resources   ☐ natural resources

3. Check the box beside each example of a natural resource.

   ☐ sunlight   ☐ air   ☐ water   ☐ pollution

   ☐ cars   ☐ books   ☐ plants   ☐ buildings

4. Wise use of natural resources is called _____ .

   ☐ pollution   ☐ conservation

5. _____ makes natural resources unfit for use by living things.

   ☐ Pollution   ☐ Conservation

6. Check the box beside each example of a renewable natural resource.

   ☐ boats   ☐ rocks   ☐ birds   ☐ schools

   ☐ water   ☐ soil   ☐ plants   ☐ trucks

Write a paragraph that tells about the importance of natural resources.

_____

_____

_____

_____

_____

_____

Home School Connection

Ask students to share what they have learned about natural and renewable resources as well as their answers on this page with a family member.

Use what you have learned to complete the sentences. Check (✓) the box next to the correct answer.

1. Not all natural resources are _____ .
   - [ ] natural
   - [ ] renewable

2. Natural resources that are used up and cannot be replaced by nature are called _____ .
   - [ ] nonrenewable resources
   - [ ] renewable resources

3. Check the box beside each example of a nonrenewable natural resource.
   - [ ] water
   - [ ] gold
   - [ ] coal
   - [ ] soil
   - [ ] natural gas
   - [ ] trees
   - [ ] oil
   - [ ] copper

4. One way to conserve minerals is through _____ .
   - [ ] pollution
   - [ ] recycling

5. Recycling is the _____ .
   - [ ] destruction of materials
   - [ ] reusing of materials

6. Materials that are not recycled are often buried in _____ .
   - [ ] landfills
   - [ ] schools

Write a paragraph that tells about the importance of recycling.

_____

_____

_____

_____

_____

_____

Home School Connection

Encourage students to share what they have learned about nonrenewable resources as well as their answers on this page with a family member.

6.60   Name

Use what you have learned to complete the sentences. Check (✓) the box next to the correct answer.

1. Natural resources that are used to produce energy are called _____ .
   ☐ energy resources   ☐ renewable

2. The three main energy resources used today are _____ .
   ☐ solar, nuclear, and wind   ☐ oil, coal, and natural gas

3. Some alternative energy resources are _____ .
   ☐ solar, nuclear, and wind   ☐ oil, coal, and natural gas

4. Some problems that we have because of our use of the main energy resources are that _____ .
   ☐ they are renewable resources and they are easy to find   ☐ they are nonrenewable resources and they cause air pollution when burned

5. The _____ is the largest single user of fossil fuels and the largest contributor to air pollution.
   ☐ conservation of electricity   ☐ generation of electricity

6. The burning of any fuel for energy produces _____ .
   ☐ air conservation   ☐ air pollution

Write a paragraph about the importance of energy resources to the world.

_____

_____

_____

_____

_____

_____

The words in the box are all examples of transportation. Write each word from the box in the correct list.

cargo ship	passenger ship	taxi	bus
freight train	car	passenger train	bicycle
cargo plane	subway	truck	airplane

Moving People

_____

_____

_____

_____

_____

Moving Goods

_____

_____

_____

_____

_____

Write a paragraph about the importance of transportation in the entire world.

_____

_____

_____

_____

_____

_____

_____

_____

Home School Connection

Have students share their categorizations and their paragraphs with a family member.

Name

Use what you have learned to complete the sentences. Check (✓) the box next to the correct answer.

1. Trains were one of the first modern forms of _____ .

   ☐ cargo   ☐ transportation

2. The transcontinental railroad connected the eastern and western United States and made _____ .

   ☐ people refuse to travel   ☐ western expansion possible

3. The first trains were run on _____ created by burning coal or oil.

   ☐ electricity   ☐ steam

4. Today most trains run on _____ .

   ☐ steam or solar energy   ☐ diesel fuel or electricity

5. Japan, Germany, and France have developed high-speed trains that can travel as fast as _____ .

   ☐ 300 miles per hour   ☐ 100 miles per hour

Write a paragraph that tells about the importance of trains as transportation for people and goods.

_____

_____

_____

_____

_____

_____

_____

Home School Connection

Encourage students to share what they have learned about trains as well as their answers on this page with a family member.

Connect each word in the box to its matching picture. Then, beneath each picture, write a sentence about that picture.

car pool

freeway

car

taxi

highway

horse and buggy

Home School Connection

Encourage students to share the information they have about automobiles with a family member.

Connect each word in the box to its matching picture. Then, beneath each picture, write a sentence about that picture.

motor boat

sail boat

boat

cargo ship

cruise ship

oil tanker

Encourage students to share the information they have about boats with a family member.

Connect each word in the box to its matching picture. Then, beneath each picture, write a sentence about that picture.

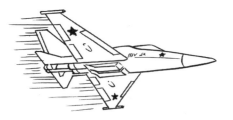

_____

_____

SST
fighter jet
space shuttle
airplane
helicopter
jet

_____

_____

_____

_____

Home School Connection

Encourage students to share the information they have about aircraft with a family member.

Using the word or phrase above each line, write a sentence that tells about communications.

Hubble Space Telescope

1. _____

radar

2. _____

navigation

3. _____

remote sensing

4. _____

satellite

5. _____

weather

6. _____

space exploration

7. _____

forecasting

8. _____

communication

9. _____

orbit

10. _____

Home School Connection

Encourage students to share what they have learned about communications as well as their sentences on this page with a family member.

Use what you have learned to complete the sentences. Check (✓) the box next to the correct answer.

1. A man named _____ invented the radio
   ☐ Edison   ☐ Marconi

2. He asked the government of _____ for money to help develop the radio, but they did not give him any.
   ☐ England   ☐ Italy

3. The first things that radios were able to send were _____ .
   ☐ messages in code   ☐ kinds of music

4. The radio was invented _____ years ago.
   ☐ 50   ☐ 100

5. The first messages were sent across the _____ Ocean.
   ☐ Atlantic   ☐ Pacific

Write a paragraph that tells about the importance of the invention of the radio.

_____

_____

_____

_____

_____

_____

_____

_____

_____

Home School Connection Encourage students to share what they have learned about the radio as well as their answers on this page with a family member.

Name

Use what you have learned to complete the sentences. Check (✓) the box next to the correct answer.

1. A man named _____ invented the telephone.

   ☐ Thomas Edison   ☐ Alexander Graham Bell

2. He invented the telephone in _____ .

   ☐ Boston, Massachusetts   ☐ Edison, New Jersey

3. The word telephone comes from Greek words that mean _____ .

   ☐ far away voice   ☐ send a sound

4. The telephone uses _____ to help send your voice to a person at the other end of the line.

   ☐ sound waves   ☐ solar energy

5. The mouthpiece of a telephone is called a _____ .

   ☐ receiver   ☐ microphone

Write a paragraph about the importance of the invention of the telephone.

_____

_____

_____

_____

_____

_____

_____

_____

Home School Connection

Encourage students to share what they have learned about the telephone as well as their answers on this page with a family member.

Using the word or phrase above each line, write a sentence that tells about television.

television camera

1. _____

electricity

2. _____

film

3. _____

news

4. _____

screen

5. _____

picture

6. _____

Russia

7. _____

information

8. _____

television

9. _____

communication

10. _____

Home School Connection

Have students read their sentences and share the information they have about television with a family member.

Use what you have learned to complete the sentences. Check (✓) the box next to the correct answer.

1. The World Wide Web is a system of information that can be viewed by anyone in the world who has access to the _____ .
   ☐ computer   ☐ Internet

2. The Internet is a system of computers that _____ with each other.
   ☐ trade   ☐ communicate

3. Many people think of the Web as a place much like a _____ .
   ☐ library   ☐ bank

4. Check the box next to each thing you can do on the Internet.
   ☐ buy goods   ☐ send letters   ☐ sell things
   ☐ watch movies   ☐ listen to music   ☐ find books

5. Today, so many people use the Internet that it has become _____ .
   ☐ outdated   ☐ one of our most importants ways to communicate

Write a paragraph that tells about the importance of the invention of the World Wide Web and the Internet.

_____

_____

_____

_____

_____

_____

_____

_____

Home School Connection Encourage students to share what they have learned about the World Wide Web and the Internet as well as their answers on this page with a family member.

Use what you have learned to complete the sentences. Check (✓) the box next to the correct answer.

1. _____ is the record of human experiences.

   ☐ Geography   ☐ History

2. Telling the stories of human experiences to others is called _____ .

   ☐ talking   ☐ oral history

3. Writing the stories of human experiences so others may read them is called _____.

   ☐ oral history   ☐ written history

4. Life before the time when writing was invented is called _____.

   ☐ prehistory   ☐ ancient

5. A person who studies or writes about history is called a _____ .

   ☐ scientist   ☐ historian

Write a paragraph about the importance of people having a written history.

_____

_____

_____

_____

_____

_____

_____

_____

_____

_____

Home School Connection   Encourage students to share what they have learned about history as well as their answers on this page with a family member.

Use what you have learned to complete the sentences. Check (✓) the box next to the correct answer.

1. The time of prehistory is also called _____ .

   ☐ the Stone Age ☐ ancient

2. Prehistory was also called the Stone Age because _____ .

   ☐ people carved their history in stone ☐ people's tools were made of stone

3. People that travel from place to place looking for food are called _____ .

   ☐ farmers ☐ nomads

4. These traveling people hunted _____ .

   ☐ bison and wooly mammoth ☐ for other people

5. One way we have learned about these ancient people is from _____ .

   ☐ their writings ☐ cave drawings

6. When they stopped being nomads, these people learned to be _____ .

   ☐ farmers ☐ writers

Write a paragraph that tells what you think life might have been like as an ancient nomad.

_____

_____

_____

_____

_____

_____

_____

_____

Home School Connection

Encourage students to share what they have learned about prehistory and the Stone Age as well as their answers on this page with a family member.

Use what you have learned to complete the sentences. Check (✓) the box next to the correct answer.

1. Over 8,000 years ago, nomads settled in an area that we now call _____ .

   ☐ the Stone Age   ☐ Mesopotamia

2. This area was located between the Tigris River and the _____ .

   ☐ Sahara Desert   ☐ Euphrates River

3. Mesopotamia means _____ .

   ☐ "the Fertile Crescent"   ☐ "the land between the rivers"

4. Three important discoveries made by the people of Mesopotamia were _____ .

   ☐ farming, ranching, and   ☐ the plow, the wheel for travel,
     transportation   and the sail

5. Part of Mesopotamia borders the _____ .

   ☐ North American continent   ☐ Mediterranean Sea

6. Many historians look on Mesopotamia as the _____ .

   ☐ birthplace of civilization   ☐ best civilization

Write sentences that tell what you think life might have been like in Ancient Mesopotamia.

_____

_____

_____

_____

_____

_____

Use what you have learned to complete the sentences. Check (✓) the box next to the correct answer.

1. The Earth's longest river is the _____ .
   ☐ Mesopotamian River   ☐ Nile River

2. This river brought water to the edge of the desert for _____ .
   ☐ 4,100 miles   ☐ 14 miles

3. Along the banks of the Nile River, the country of _____ began.
   ☐ Mesopotamia   ☐ Egypt

4. Egypt's people believed their ruler was like a god and he was called a _____ .
   ☐ pharoah   ☐ nomad

5. The Egyptians developed a system of writing called _____ .
   ☐ hieroglyphics   ☐ communications

6. The Egyptians built many structures called _____ , some of which are standing today.
   ☐ pyramids   ☐ Nile

Write a paragraph that tells what you think life might have been like in Ancient Egypt.

_____

_____

_____

_____

_____

_____

Home School Connection   Encourage students to share what they have learned about Ancient Egypt as well as their answers on this page with a family member.

Name

Use what you have learned to complete the sentences. Check (✓) the box next to the correct answer.

1. Just south of Ancient Egypt was a kingdom called Kush, but today it is called _____.
☐ Mesopotamia   ☐ Sudan

2. Like Egypt, the people in Kush had the _____ that helped their kingdom grow.
☐ farmers   ☐ Nile River

3. The people of Kush traded _____ with the Egyptians
☐ rice, meat, and musical instruments   ☐ grain, gold, and slaves

4. When Egypt's pharoah led an army to take over Kush, _____ .
☐ Egypt won the battle and Kush became a part of Egypt   ☐ Kush won the battle and Egypt became a part of Kush

5. The people in Kush built pyramids, but they had _____ .
☐ flat tops   ☐ pointed tops

6. The people of Kush developed their own system of _____ , but we don't understand it today.
☐ money   ☐ writing

Write a paragraph that tells what you think life might have been like in Ancient Kush.

_____

_____

_____

_____

_____

_____

_____

Home School Connection

Encourage students to share what they have learned about Ancient Kush as well as their answers on this page with a family member.

Use what you have learned to complete the sentences. Check (✓) the box next to the correct answer.

1. The Hebrews were an ancient people who lived in _____ .

   ☐ Kush ☐ Judah

2. The Hebrews were the first people to believe in the idea of _____ .

   ☐ one god ☐ trading

3. The idea of one god is called _____ .

   ☐ Judah ☐ monotheism

4. Egypt conquered the Hebrews and they became _____ .

   ☐ old ☐ slaves

5. Judah was located in _____ .

   ☐ the Fertile Crescent ☐ Egypt

6. We get much of the history of the ancient Hebrews from _____ .

   ☐ cave drawings ☐ the Bible

Write a paragraph that tells what you think life might have been like in Ancient Judah.

_____

_____

_____

_____

_____

_____

_____

_____

Home School Connection Encourage students to share what they have learned about the Hebrews as well as their answers on this page with a family member.

Use what you have learned to complete the sentences. Check (✓) the box next to the correct answer.

1. The earliest settlement in the Greek region started on the island of Crete in the
   _____ .

   ☐ desert   ☐ Mediterranean Sea

2. Because there were so many mountains in Greece, the people traveled a lot by
   _____.

   ☐ camel   ☐ boat

3. The Greeks had many gods and believed that these gods lived on _____ .

   ☐ Crete   ☐ Mount Olympus

4. We have borrowed Greece's system of government called a _____.

   ☐ monotheism   ☐ democracy

5. The father of modern democracy could be an ancient Greek named _____ .

   ☐ Olympus   ☐ Solon

6. The _____ we have today are a kind of games like the ancient Greeks had.

   ☐ battles   ☐ Olympics

Write a paragraph that tells what you think life might have been like in Ancient Greece.

_____

_____

_____

_____

_____

_____

_____

6.78   Name

Use what you have learned to complete the sentences. Check (✓) the box next to the correct answer.

1. The earliest civilization in India was between _____ .
   ☐ the Fertile Crescent and the   ☐ two sets of mountains
       Mediterranean Sea

2. Bronze is a metal that is a combination of _____ .
   ☐ copper and tin   ☐ iron and steel

3. The people of ancient India believed in _____ .
   ☐ one god   ☐ many gods

4. The people were divided into four groups called _____ to serve the gods.
   ☐ tribes   ☐ castes

5. People born into one caste _____ .
   ☐ never changed their caste   ☐ changed castes often

6. The Taj Mahal is a _____ .
   ☐ palace   ☐ tomb built for a beautiful woman

Write a paragraph that tells what you think life might have been like in Ancient India.

_____

_____

_____

_____

_____

_____

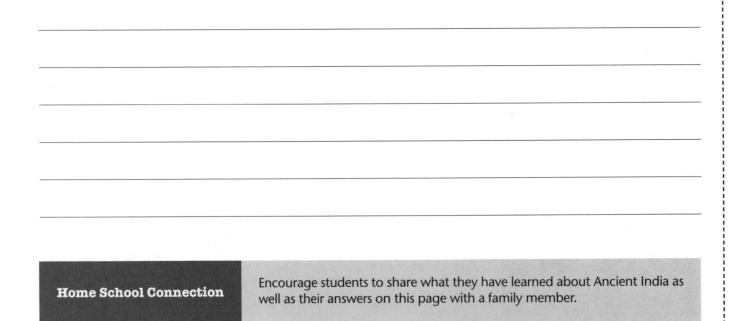

Home School Connection

Encourage students to share what they have learned about Ancient India as well as their answers on this page with a family member.

Use what you have learned to complete the sentences. Check (✓) the box next to the correct answer.

1. China's civilization goes back at least 7,000 years and is _____ .
   ☐ the oldest continuous culture in history
   ☐ the newest continuous culture in history

2. The ancient Chinese began to believe that they were _____ .
   ☐ going to lose the wars they fought
   ☐ superior to other peoples

3. The man who conquered the peoples of China called himself _____ .
   ☐ the first emperor
   ☐ superior

4. The emperor Qin joined walls together to make _____ .
   ☐ a castle
   ☐ the Great Wall of China

5. The Chinese people traded food and _____ with people far away.
   ☐ wheat
   ☐ silk

6. The Chinese invented many things including _____ .
   ☐ food, rice, weaving, and silk
   ☐ printing, gunpowder, silk, and the compass

Write a paragraph that tells what you think life might have been like in Ancient China.

_____

_____

_____

_____

_____

_____

_____

Home School Connection

Encourage students to share what they have learned about Ancient China as well as their answers on this page with a family member.

Using all the words in the box, write several paragraphs about life in Ancient Rome.

aqueduct	Italy	republic	plumbing	citizen
public baths	Etruscans	Augustus	conquer	

_____

_____

_____

_____

_____

_____

_____

_____

_____

_____

_____

_____

_____

_____

_____

_____

_____

Using the word or phrase above each line, write a sentence that tells about the Seven Wonders of the Ancient World.

art

1. _____

architecture

2. _____

amazing

3. _____

civilization

4. _____

ancient

5. _____

wonders

6. _____

temple

7. _____

colossus

8. _____

pyramid

9. _____

mausoleum

10. _____

Home School Connection

Have students read their sentences and share the information they have on the Seven Wonders of the Ancient World with a family member.

Use what you have learned to complete the sentences. Check (✓) the box next to the correct answer.

1. The Great Pyramid is the only one of the Seven Wonders of the Ancient World that is still standing today and it is the _____ of the wonders.
   - [ ] newest
   - [ ] oldest

2. The Great Pyramid is located at _____ .
   - [ ] Giza in Egypt
   - [ ] Mesopotamia on the Mediterranean Sea

3. It was built as a _____ for the Pharoah Khufu.
   - [ ] temple
   - [ ] tomb

4. It took 20 years and _____ people to build the Great Pyramid.
   - [ ] 10,000
   - [ ] 100,000

5. Khufu's _____ , or coffin, was placed in the burial chamber.
   - [ ] chamber
   - [ ] sarcophagus

6. Until the 1800s, the Great Pyramid was the _____ structure on Earth.
   - [ ] strongest
   - [ ] tallest

In the box below, make a sketch of what you think the Great Pyramid looked like when it was new.

Home School Connection

Encourage students to share what they have learned about the Great Pyramid as well as their answers on this page with a family member.

Use what you have learned to complete the sentences. Check (✓) the box next to the correct answer.

1. The Colossus of Rhodes was _____ .

☐ a memorial at Giza   ☐ a statue of Helios

2. The people of Rhodes built the Colossus to _____ .

☐ celebrate their victory in winning their freedom   ☐ act as a lighthouse for sailors coming into the city

3. Colossus means _____ .

☐ a huge statue   ☐ a memorial

4. The statue was _____ feet high and stood on a 50-foot pedestal.

☐ 100   ☐ 1,000

5. The people of Rhodes considered Helios to be their _____ .

☐ god   ☐ pharoah

6. 56 years after the Colossus of Rhodes was built, it was destroyed by _____ .

☐ a war   ☐ an earthquake

In the box below, make a sketch of what you think the Colossus of Rhodes looked like.

Home School Connection   Encourage students to share what they have learned about the Colossus of Rhodes as well as their answers on this page with a family member.

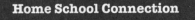

Use what you have learned to complete the sentences. Check (✓) the box next to the correct answer.

1. The Statue of Zeus at Olympia was built around _____ .
   ☐ 457 B.C.   ☐ 457 A.D.

2. Zeus was a Greek god who was thought to be _____ .
   ☐ ruler of all the Greeks   ☐ king of all the gods

3. In the statue, Zeus is _____ .
   ☐ in the middle of a war   ☐ sitting on his throne

4. The statue was as tall as a _____ .
   ☐ three-story building   ☐ four-story building

5. The first Olympic games were held at _____ .
   ☐ Olympia   ☐ Egypt

6. In 462 A.D., the Statue of Zeus at Olympia was destroyed by _____ .
   ☐ a fire   ☐ an earthquake

In the box below, make a sketch of what you think the Statue of Zeus at Olympia looked like.

Home School Connection

Encourage students to share what they have learned about the Statue of Zeus at Olympia as well as their answers on this page with a family member.

Use what you have learned to complete the sentences. Check (✓) the box next to the correct answer.

1. King _____ ruled a small kingdom on the Mediterranean Sea.

   ☐ Mausolus ☐ Halicarnassus

2. When the king died, Queen Artemisia decided to have a spectacular _____ built as a way of honoring his memory.

   ☐ temple ☐ tomb

3. There were _____ on both sides of the stairs leading to the tomb.

   ☐ lions ☐ chariots

4. The roof was shaped like a _____ .

   ☐ horse-drawn carriage ☐ pyramid

5. At the very top of the roof was a _____ with statues of two people in it .

   ☐ tomb ☐ chariot

6. The tomb of King Mausolus became so famous that the word mausoleum comes from his name and means _____ .

   ☐ a large and impressive tomb ☐ a spectacular temple

In the box below, make a sketch of what you think the Mausoleum at Halicarnassus looked like.

Home School Connection

Encourage students to share what they have learned about the Mausoleum at Halicarnassus as well as their answers on this page with a family member.

Name

Use what you have learned to complete the sentences. Check (✓) the box next to the correct answer.

1. _____ was the Greek goddess of the hunt.

☐ Ephesus   ☐ Artemis

2. The Temple of Artemis was begun shortly after 356 B.C. in _____ .

☐ Ephesus   ☐ Artemis

3. Some records say that it took _____ to build the temple.

☐ 120 years   ☐ 120 days

4. The temple was one of the first buildings to be made entirely out of _____ .

☐ bricks   ☐ marble

5. The temple was built on _____ .

☐ a hill   ☐ marshy land

6. In 262 A.D., the Goths _____ the temple.

☐ invaded the city and destroyed   ☐ left gifts for Artemis in

In the box below, make a sketch of what you think the Temple of Artemis looked like.

Use what you have learned to complete the sentences. Check (✓) the box next to the correct answer.

1. The Great Lighthouse of Alexandria in Egypt was built on the ancient island of

   _____ .

   ☐ Egypt   ☐ Pharos

2. The Great Lighthouse of Alexandria is also known as the _____ .

   ☐ Pharos Lighthouse   ☐ Egyptian Lighthouse

3. It was more like a city _____ than a lighthouse.

   ☐ street   ☐ skyscraper

4. The lighthouse was about _____ tall.

   ☐ 4 stories   ☐ 40 stories

5. A fire burned at the top of the lighthouse and a _____ a beam to ships.

   ☐ man sent   ☐ mirror reflected

6. Horse-drawn carriages drove along a _____ to carry materials into the lighthouse.

   ☐ wide street   ☐ spiral ramp

In the box below, make a sketch of what you think the Lighthouse of Alexandria looked like.

Use what you have learned to complete the sentences. Check (✓) the box next to the correct answer.

1. King Nebuchadnezzar ruled _____ from 605 B.C. until 562 B.C.

   ☐ Babylon   ☐ Greece

2. Nebuchadnezzar married Amyitis, the daughter of the King of Medes because _____ .

   ☐ he was in love with her   ☐ he and the King of Medes wanted to build an alliance

3. Amyitis missed the green mountains of her home so King Nebuchadnezzar had the hanging gardens built to _____ .

   ☐ take her there   ☐ cheer her up

4. The gardens were _____ so they would remind Amyitis of the mountains.

   ☐ terraced   ☐ large

5. The trees and plants did not hang from the sky, but _____ of the terraces.

   ☐ over the sides   ☐ under the sides

6. Slaves used a special _____ to bring water to the garden from the river.

   ☐ water bucket   ☐ water pump

In the box below, make a sketch of what you think the Hanging Gardens of Babylon looked like.

Use what you have learned to complete the sentences. Check (✓) the box next to the correct answer.

1. If all Seven Wonders still existed today, the _____ would be the oldest.
   - [ ] Hanging Gardens of Babylon
   - [ ] Great Pyramid of Giza

2. The Colossus of Rhodes and the Statue of Zeus at Halicarnassus are both _____ .
   - [ ] statues
   - [ ] temples

3. The last of the Seven Wonders to be built was _____ .
   - [ ] The Colossus of Rhodes
   - [ ] The Lighthouse of Alexandria

4. The smallest of the Seven Wonders was _____ .
   - [ ] The Temple of Artemis
   - [ ] The Statue of Zeus at Olympia

5. We don't know how long the Hanging Gardens of Babylon lasted, but the _____ survived for only 56 years.
   - [ ] Mausoleum at Halicarnassus
   - [ ] Colossus of Rhodes

6. _____ was 225 feet wide and 425 feet long.
   - [ ] The Temple of Artemis
   - [ ] The Great Pyramid of Giza

Write a paragraph about which of the Seven Wonders you would most like to have seen. Be sure to tell why you would want to see that particular Wonder.

_____

_____

_____

_____

_____

_____

_____

Home School Connection

Encourage students to share what they have learned and their sentences about the Seven Wonders with a family member.

Name

Use what you have learned to complete the sentences. Check (✓) the box next to the correct answer.

1. The _____ was on an island in the Mediterranean Sea.
   ☐ Colossus of Rhodes   ☐ Statue of Zeus at Olympia

2. Both the Lighthouse at Alexandria and the Great Pyramid of Giza were in _____ .
   ☐ Greece   ☐ Egypt

3. The _____ were furthest away from the Mediterranean Sea.
   ☐ Colossus of Rhodes   ☐ Hanging Gardens of Babylon

4. The Statue of Zeus at Olympia was in _____ .
   ☐ Asia Minor   ☐ Greece

5. All of the Wonders were close to the Mediterranean Sea except for _____ .
   ☐ the Mausoleum at Halicarnassus and the Colossus of Rhodes   ☐ the Great Pyramid of Giza and the Hanging Gardens of Babylon

6. _____ was the closest of the Seven Wonders to Crete.
   ☐ The Mausoleum at Halicarnassus   ☐ The Colossus of Rhodes

Write a paragraph telling about the Eighth Wonder that you would build. Be sure to describe what your Wonder looks like.

_____

_____

_____

_____

_____

_____

_____

Home School Connection

Encourage students to share what they have learned and their sentences about the Eighth Wonder with a family member.

Use what you have learned to complete the sentences. Check (✓) the box next to the correct answer.

1. A _____ is formed when an organized group of people living in one place makes rules for everyone who lives there.
   ☐ citizen ☐ government

2. The people who live in a country under one government are called _____ .
   ☐ citizens ☐ voters

3. One way that a government can serve its citizens is _____ .
   ☐ protecting their lives and property ☐ operating businesses

4. Citizens expect their government to be responsible for _____ .
   ☐ telling them what to do ☐ enforcing laws

5. Governments of different kinds have existed for _____ .
   ☐ hundreds of years ☐ thousands of years

6. One example of a person who works for a government is a _____ .
   ☐ shopkeeper ☐ soldier

Fill in the blank spaces to complete the statements.

1. I live in the state of _____ .
2. The capital of my state is _____ .
3. The capital of the United States of America is _____ .

Use what you have learned to complete the sentences. Check (✓) the box next to the correct answer.

1. A form of government in which the people make the laws and run the government is called a _____ .

   ☐ constitution ☐ democracy

2. The idea of democracy came from _____ .

   ☐ ancient Greece ☐ ancient Egypt

3. A written plan of government is called a _____ .

   ☐ constitution ☐ democracy

4. In a democracy, everyone is _____ .

   ☐ equal ☐ superior

5. In a _____ , the citizens vote to elect representatives to run the country.

   ☐ republic ☐ state

6. The United States of America is both a democracy and a _____ .

   ☐ republic ☐ constitution

On the lines below, make a list of some of the rights and freedoms that the United States Constitution guarantees its citizens.

_____

_____

_____

_____

_____

_____

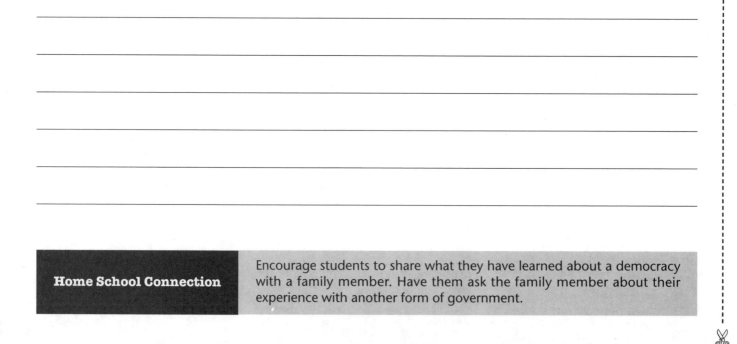

Home School Connection

Encourage students to share what they have learned about a democracy with a family member. Have them ask the family member about their experience with another form of government.

Use what you have learned to complete the sentences. Check (✓) the box next to the correct answer.

1. A form of government in which the power comes from the people is called a _____ .
   ☐ republic   ☐ democracy

2. In a republic, the people elect _____ .
   ☐ a king   ☐ representatives

3. In the United States, citizens elect representatives to _____ .
   ☐ build highways   ☐ pass laws and run a democratic government

4. In the United States, people _____ for the persons they want to send to the House of Representatives and the Senate.
   ☐ ask   ☐ vote

5. A republic is a form of government that allows citizens to choose _____ to rule for them.
   ☐ representatives   ☐ citizens

6. Any American citizen who is _____ years old can vote for the representatives they wish to send to the House of Representatives and the Senate.
   ☐ 18   ☐ 21

7. In the United States, the House of Representatives and the Senate are referred to as _____ .
   ☐ Government   ☐ Congress

8. When America declared its independence from England, the American people decided that they did not want a _____ .
   ☐ government   ☐ king

Home School Connection Encourage students to share what they have learned about a republic with a family member.

6.94

Name

Use what you have learned to complete the sentences. Check (✓) the box next to the correct answer.

1. Communism is a form of government that began in _____ in 1921.

   ☐ Greece   ☐ Russia

2. Working class people in Russia were not happy with the _____ .

   ☐ communists   ☐ Czar

3. Communism is a political system in which the government owns most _____ and then the people share the property.

   ☐ people   ☐ property

4. Many of the _____ people in Russia liked the idea of communism because they thought they would be able to share in more of Russia's wealth.

   ☐ ruling class   ☐ working class

5. When communists took control of Russia, their leader was a man named _____ .

   ☐ Czar   ☐ Lenin

6. Communism became the form of government in other countries such as _____ .

   ☐ Canada, England, and Australia   ☐ China, Cuba, and North Korea

7. Under communism, citizens _____ make the laws or choose representatives to run the country.

   ☐ do   ☐ don't

8. Communism remained the form of _____ in Russia until 1991.

   ☐ government   ☐ congress

Name

Use what you have learned to complete the sentences. Check (✓) the box next to the correct answer.

1. A monarchy is a form of government headed by one ruler, usually a _____ .
   ☐ Senate or House of Representatives   ☐ king or queen

2. The king or queen is often called a _____ .
   ☐ citizen   ☐ monarch

3. In a monarchy, the king or queen has a right to rule during his or her _____ .
   ☐ lifetime   ☐ term

4. In a monarchy, the king or queen would have to _____ before a new king or queen could rule.
   ☐ be removed by an election   ☐ die or step down

5. In many monarchies, the king or queen has absolute power, which means that _____ makes all the decisions and has all the power.
   ☐ the Senate   ☐ one person

6. Monarchies have been used as a form of _____ for many hundreds of years.
   ☐ government   ☐ election

7. Some countries have a democratic monarchy in which the monarch is the living symbol of the nation, but the monarch does not have _____ .
   ☐ absolute power   ☐ any power

8. Denmark, Belgium, Great Britain, Spain, Norway, Sweden, and the Netherlands have a _____ as their form of government.
   ☐ absolute monarchy   ☐ democratic monarchy

Name

Use what you have learned to complete the sentences. Check (✓) the box next to the correct answer.

1. An oligarchy is a form of government in which _____ rule over many people .
   - [ ] a king and queen
   - [ ] a few people

2. An oligarchy is similar to a monarchy, except that instead of just _____ there are a few rulers who share power.
   - [ ] one ruler
   - [ ] many rulers

3. Sometimes an oligarchy is made up of powerful _____ called generals.
   - [ ] kings
   - [ ] military leaders

4. These military leaders use the strength of _____ to gain power over the people.
   - [ ] elections
   - [ ] armies

5. Oligarchies were found in Western _____ during the Middle Ages from about 500 to 1500 AD.
   - [ ] United States
   - [ ] Europe

6. During the Middle Ages, the wealthiest people were those who owned _____ .
   - [ ] cattle
   - [ ] land

7. Wealthy landowners, called _____ ruled over an area and often shared power with other wealthy landowners.
   - [ ] kings
   - [ ] lords

8. Although there are few oligarchies in existence today, they are still the major form of _____ in some countries, such as Myanmar.
   - [ ] government
   - [ ] trade

Home School Connection   Encourage students to share what they have learned about an oligarchy with a family member.

Use what you have learned to complete the sentences. Check (✓) the box next to the correct answer.

1. Beginning in the 1400s, powerful countries such as France, England, Italy, and Spain wanted to increase their _____ by claiming new lands outside of their boundaries.

   ☐ population   ☐ power

2. _____ were sent to search for new lands to settle.

   ☐ Governors   ☐ Explorers

3. These new settlements were called _____ .

   ☐ islands   ☐ colonies

4. The country that claimed the colony governed the people who came to live in the colony and were called _____ .

   ☐ citizens   ☐ colonists

5. This form of governing, often over great distances, is called _____ .

   ☐ an oligarchy   ☐ colonialism

6. These new _____ supplied the ruling country with raw materials such as oil, rubber, tin, cotton, tea, wheat, gold, and other valuable products.

   ☐ farmers   ☐ colonies

7. In the 1800s, _____ was Great Britain's most important colony.

   ☐ France   ☐ India

8. Holland, Spain, Italy, Portugal, France, and Great Britain all established colonies in _____ .

   ☐ England   ☐ Africa

Home School Connection

Encourage students to share what they have learned about colonialism with a family member.

Use what you have learned to complete the sentences. Check (✓) the box next to the correct answer.

1. A _____ is the lawmaking body of a nation.
   ☐ government   ☐ parliament

2. A parliament is made up of people who are _____ by the citizens of a nation to make and vote on laws.
   ☐ elected   ☐ represented

3. The oldest existing parliament in the world that is still working today is in _____ .
   ☐ France   ☐ Great Britain

4. Parliament began in England during the 1200s when a group of powerful people forced the King of England to sign a document called the _____ .
   ☐ Bill of Rights   ☐ Magna Carta

5. The Magna Carta was a list of changes in government that the people of England _____ .
   ☐ demanded   ☐ had voted for

6. One thing that the people wanted in England was for the common man to have a say in making _____ for the country.
   ☐ money   ☐ laws

7. England has two houses of _____ – the House of Lords and the House of Commons.
   ☐ Parliament   ☐ government

8. The United States has a _____ made up of two parts – the Senate and the House of Representatives.
   ☐ Parliament   ☐ Congress

Use what you have learned to complete the sentences. Check (✓) the box next to the correct answer.

1. In today's world, _____ often work together to help each other in many ways.
   ☐ kings   ☐ nations

2. Nations often share _____ such as exciting discoveries in the fields of health and medicine.
   ☐ governments   ☐ information

3. People who are officials and represent their country in work with another country are called _____ .
   ☐ diplomats   ☐ doctors

4. Diplomats often meet to talk about a way in which to resolve their differences peacefully through a _____ .
   ☐ bill of rights   ☐ treaty

5. A treaty is an _____ that is written down and signed by two or more groups.
   ☐ international organization   ☐ agreement

6. Diplomats from 185 nations meet at _____ , whose headquarters are in New York City.
   ☐ the United Nations   ☐ work

7. The United Nations is an _____ that works to preserve, or keep world peace.
   ☐ international organization   ☐ agreement

8. Diplomats meet at the United Nations every day to discuss world problems and look for _____ .
   ☐ treaties   ☐ solutions

Home School Connection

Encourage students to share what they have learned about diplomacy with a family member.

Using the word or phrase above each line, write a sentence about government.

Washington, D.C.

1. _____

citizen

2. _____

city hall

3. _____

community

4. _____

law

5. _____

protect

6. _____

state

7. _____

local

8. _____

municipal building

9. _____

unite

10. _____

Home School Connection   Have students read their sentences and share the information they have on people and government with a family member.

You have learned about economics. Fill in the blank lines in each box with examples of the kinds of jobs people have, the kinds of goods people make, and the kinds of services people offer. In each box, the first one is done for you.

Jobs People Have

delivering groceries   _____   _____

_____   _____   _____

_____   _____   _____

_____   _____   _____

Goods People Make

telephones   _____   _____

_____   _____   _____

_____   _____   _____

_____   _____   _____

Services People Offer

babysitting   _____   _____

_____   _____   _____

_____   _____   _____

_____   _____   _____

Home School Connection

Have students share their lists of jobs, goods, and services with a family member. Have the student discuss with the family member whether the jobs are for producing goods or offering services.

Name

You have learned about resources and how we use resources to meet our needs. In each box is a natural resource. On the lines connected to the box, write the names of products that come from that natural resource. Each list has been started for you.

Trees

notebook paper

Oil

plastic drinking cup

Using the word above each line, write a sentence that tells about agriculture.

cattle

1. _____

cheese

2. _____

corn

3. _____

farm

4. _____

sheep

5. _____

soil

6. _____

crop

7. _____

cultivate

8. _____

harvest

9. _____

dairy

10. _____

Home School Connection   Have students read their sentences and share the information they have on agriculture with a family member.

Use what you have learned about forests and forestry to write a short story about your responsibilities and challenges as the manager of a forest.

_____

_____

_____

_____

_____

_____

_____

_____

_____

_____

_____

_____

_____

_____

_____

_____

_____

_____

_____

_____

_____

_____

Home School Connection   Have students share their short stories with a family member.

You have learned about mining and the mining industry. In the box below are items that can be placed in one of two lists. Write the word in the Out of the Ground list if it comes directly from a mine. If the word is something that is manufactured from a mineral, write it in the Manufactured with Minerals list. The first one in each list is done for you.

gold nugget	coal lump	copper nugget	chunk	gold chain
gold bracelet	charcoal pencil	copper wire
chalk	silver ring	silver nugget	uncut diamond
diamond necklace	chalk marker	gemstones	opal ring

Out of the Ground	**Manufactured with Minerals**
coal lump	*charcoal pencil*

Make a list of 10 other things that are manufactured from minerals.

Home School Connection

Encourage students to share their lists with a family member and add other items that the family member might suggest.

Name

You have learned about fishing and the fishing industry. Using the word or phrase above each line, write a sentence about fishing or the fishing industry.

fish

1. _____

_____

salt water

2. _____

_____

shellfish

3. _____

_____

fresh water

4. _____

_____

ocean

5. _____

_____

catching

6. _____

_____

net

7. _____

_____

Home School Connection

Encourage students to share their sentences and information they have about fishing and the fishing industry with a family member.

Name

You have learned about manufacturing and the manufacturing industry. On the lines, write the names of as many raw materials that you can think of that went into the manufacture of the backpack.

_____   _____

_____   _____

_____   _____

In the space below, draw a sketch of something that could be manufactured from one square yard of cotton cloth, one zipper, and two rubber bands. You may add any other materials you choose, but you must use all the materials from this list. Be sure to give a title to your invention.

Name

You have learned about currency. Using the word above each line, write a sentence about currency.

dollar

1. _____

_____

money

2. _____

_____

currency

3. _____

_____

exchange

4. _____

_____

barter

5. _____

_____

purchase

6. _____

_____

trade

7. _____

_____

Home School Connection Encourage students to share their sentences and information they have about currency with a family member.

You have learned about importing goods. Above each numbered line, write the name of something that is imported into the United States. Then, for each imported product, write a sentence about who might use it or how it might be used.

_____

1. _____

_____

_____

2. _____

_____

_____

3. _____

_____

_____

4. _____

_____

_____

5. _____

_____

_____

6. _____

_____

Home School Connection

Encourage students to share their sentences and the information they have about importing with a family member.

You have learned about exporting goods. Using each word or phrase above the line, write a sentence about exporting.

freighter

1. _____

_____

truck

2. _____

_____

cargo plane

3. _____

_____

freight train

4. _____

_____

shortage

5. _____

_____

surplus

6. _____

_____

trade

7. _____

_____

Home School Connection   Encourage students to share their sentences and the information they have about exporting with a family member.

Each invention listed in the boxes below has changed our world. But there is always room for improvement. In each box, write a sentence that suggests an improvement on the invention that you think would make it better.

airplane

_____

_____

_____

telephone

_____

_____

_____

television

_____

_____

_____

computer

_____

_____

_____

space shuttle

_____

_____

_____

You have learned about how wars change our world. Using each word or phrase above the line, write a sentence about war.

soldier

1. _____

_____

United Nations

2. _____

_____

alliance

3. _____

_____

battle

4. _____

_____

disagreement

5. _____

_____

power

6. _____

_____

treaties

7. _____

_____

Home School Connection

Encourage students to share their sentences and the information they have about war with a family member. Have students talk about any wartime experiences the family members may have had.

Name

Use what you have learned to complete the sentences. Check (✓) the box next to the correct answer.

1. Before the invention of the _____ , every book was written by hand.
   - [ ] automobile
   - [ ] printing press

2. When every book was written by hand, it was done by specially trained people called _____ .
   - [ ] scribes
   - [ ] printers

3. When books were written by hand, only churches and _____ could afford to own these rare books.
   - [ ] wealthy families
   - [ ] politicians

4. In 1450, _____ invented a machine that could print with moveable letters carved out of metal that could be arranged on a plate.
   - [ ] Jacques Cousteau
   - [ ] Johannes Gutenberg

5. Because of the printing press, more people could have books and learn to read because books cost a lot ____ _____ .
   - [ ] less
   - [ ] more

In the box below, create an advertisement for the new printed books that appeared in 1450.

In a few years, you will be old enough to take a driving test and get a driver's license. By that time, cars will have changed from how they are today. In the space below, draw a sketch of the car you would like to have, and write a paragraph describing how having that car will change your life.

_____

_____

_____

_____

_____

_____

_____

You have learned how airplanes have changed our lives. Using each word above the line, write a sentence about flight or air travel.

airport

1. _____

_____

helicopter

2. _____

_____

jet

3. _____

_____

commerce

4. _____

_____

hangar

5. _____

_____

aviation

6. _____

_____

fly

7. _____

_____

Home School Connection

Encourage students to share their sentences and information they have about air travel and commerce with a family member.

Name

If you had to choose the programs that would be shown on television, what would they be? In the boxes below, write the names or descriptions of television programs that you would and would not broadcast.

My Television Programming List

The Programs I Would Broadcast	The Programs I Would Not Broadcast
1._____	1._____
2._____	2._____
3._____	3._____
4._____	4._____
5._____	5._____
6._____	6._____
7._____	7._____
8._____	8._____
9._____	9._____
10._____	10._____

My all-time favorite television program is_____

The best thing about that program is _____

If I could choose new actors for that program, they would be _____

_____

The program I think should never be on television is_____

_____

Home School Connection

Encourage students to share their programming lists with a family member and to compare their opinions.

NASA is planning a space flight to explore Saturn's rings and they have asked you to go along. Write a short story about your adventure in space.

_____

_____

_____

_____

_____

_____

_____

_____

_____

_____

_____

_____

_____

_____

_____

_____

_____

_____

_____

Name

Use the words from the box to write several paragraphs about how medicine has changed our world.

laboratory	vaccine	disease	dose	infection
scientist	immunize	research	treatment	

_____

_____

_____

_____

_____

_____

_____

_____

_____

_____

_____

_____

_____

_____

_____

_____

Home School Connection   Encourage students to share their writing with a family member.

Computers have made life easier for people by helping them do things that were too difficult to do. But some things are still better not done by computer. On the lines below, make two lists. The first list should be things that are easier to do because of computers. The second list should be things that are just as easy to do without a computer.

It is easier to do these things if you have a computer:

1. _____
2. _____
3. _____
4. _____
5. _____
6. _____
7. _____
8. _____
9. _____
10. _____

You don't really need a computer to do these things:

1. _____
2. _____
3. _____
4. _____
5. _____
6. _____
7. _____
8. _____
9. _____
10. _____

Use what you have learned to complete the sentences. Check (✓) the box next to the correct answer.

1. The Internet is a network that can link computers around the world together in one _____ system.
   - ☐ e-mail
   - ☐ communication

2. The idea for the Internet started in _____ .
   - ☐ 1973
   - ☐ 1993

3. Soon after its creation, researchers at _____ started to use the technology to send e-mail and other information to other researchers around the world.
   - ☐ universities
   - ☐ television stations

4. Invented early in the 1990s, the World Wide Web uses a special _____ that allows us to add sound and pictures to the information sent over the Internet.
   - ☐ computer
   - ☐ language

5. The Internet carries so much information that it is called the _____ .
   - ☐ World Wide Web
   - ☐ Information Superhighway

Make a list of some of the things a person can do over the Internet.

_____

_____

_____

_____

_____

_____

_____

_____

Home School Connection

Encourage students to share what they have learned about the Internet with a family member.

Name

Put an **X** over each lesson you have completed in **Santillana Intensive English**.

Unit 1	6.1	6.2	6.3	6.4	6.5	6.6	6.7	6.8	6.9	6.10
Unit 2	6.11	6.12	6.13	6.14	6.15	6.16	6.17	6.18	6.19	6.20
Unit 3	6.21	6.22	6.23	6.24	6.25	6.26	6.27	6.28	6.29	6.30
Unit 4	6.31	6.32	6.33	6.34	6.35	6.36	6.37	6.38	6.39	6.40
Unit 5	6.41	6.42	6.43	6.44	6.45	6.46	6.47	6.48	6.49	6.50
Unit 6	6.51	6.52	6.53	6.54	6.55	6.56	6.57	6.58	6.59	6.60
Unit 7	6.61	6.62	6.63	6.64	6.65	6.66	6.67	6.68	6.69	6.70
Unit 8	6.71	6.72	6.73	6.74	6.75	6.76	6.77	6.78	6.79	6.80
Unit 9	6.81	6.82	6.83	6.84	6.85	6.86	6.87	6.88	6.89	6.90
Unit 10	6.91	6.92	6.93	6.94	6.95	6.96	6.97	6.98	6.99	6.100
Unit 11	6.101	6.102	6.103	6.104	6.105	6.106	6.107	6.108	6.109	6.110
Unit 12	6.111	6.112	6.113	6.114	6.115	6.116	6.117	6.118	6.119	6.120

Este libro se terminó de imprimir en el mes de octubre de 2001, en Litográfica Ingramex, S.A. de C.V., Centeno 162, Col. Granjas Esmeralda, 09810 México, D.F.